MORE ROMANTIC PIECES FOR

Edited by LIONEL SALTER

BOOK I

The pieces in this book are about Grades 1 and 2 in standard (Associated Board)
Metronome marks within square brackets are editorial

THE ASSOCIATED BOARD OF THE ROYAL SCHOOLS OF MUSIC

ECOSSAISE

WEBER

Weber (Mozart's cousin by marriage) led an unsettled existence in his youth, as his father was music director of a travelling theatre company. This Ecossaise is one of six he wrote at the age of 16 and dedicated 'to the fair sex in Hamburg'. The LH part in bars 8 and 24 is editorial.

ALLEGRETTO

CZERNY, Op.599 No.36

Karl Czerny, a favourite pupil of Beethoven (who at one time contemplated living in his house) and the teacher of Liszt, was enormously prolific in every sphere of music but is remembered today almost solely for his numerous educational works for piano.

LÄNDLER

SCHUBERT, D.679 No.2

Schubert wrote over 400 dance pieces, many actually intended for his friends to dance to. This Ländler (an Austrian country dance) is one of two that he wrote about 1820.

STUDY IN D

BERTINI, Op.137 No.9

Though of a French family and himself resident in France (where he made a reputation as a pianist) from the age of 23, Henri Bertini was born in London. Precociously gifted, he was taught by his brother, a pupil of Clementi, and at the age of 12 made an extensive concert tour of the Low Countries and Germany.

ANDANTINO

J.-B. DUVERNOY, Op.176 No.15

Member of a large family of French musicians, several of whom were professors at the Paris Conservatoire, Jean-Baptiste Duvernoy wrote hundreds of pieces and studies for piano.

ANDANTE

ENCKHAUSEN, Op.93 No.22

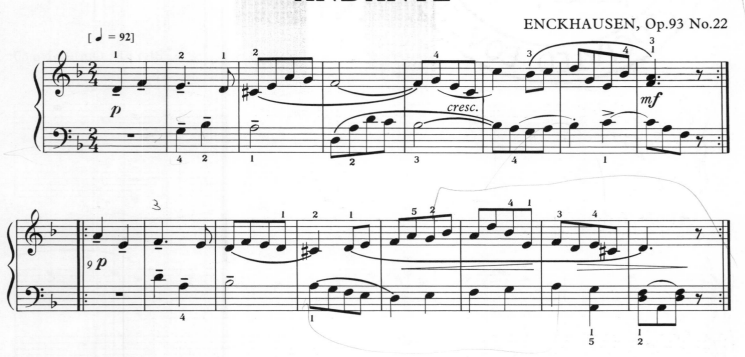

ALLEGRETTO

ENCKHAUSEN, Op.93 No.33

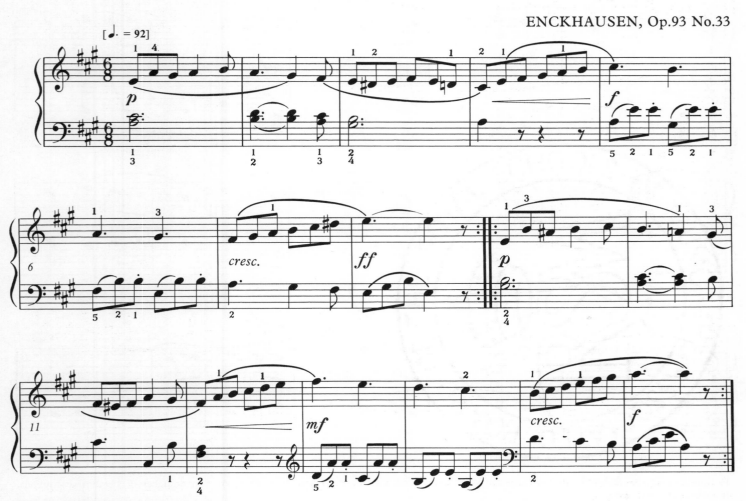

Heinrich Enckhausen was a teacher in Hanover who wrote a large quantity of easy piano pieces and educational music.

AB 2077

ANDANTE

F. BEYER, Op.101 No.60

Ferdinand Beyer was employed in his native town of Mainz by the publishing house of Schott, for which he wrote huge numbers of operatic transcriptions, fantasias, pot-pourris, etc.

ARABESQUE

BURGMÜLLER, Op.100 No.2

Johann Burgmüller's father was a conductor and his younger brother a gifted composer who died tragically young: he himself, born in Regensburg, settled in Paris and wrote numerous salon pieces and studies that have become familiar to generations of teachers and students.

AB 2077

SOLDIERS' MARCH

SCHUMANN, Op.68 No.2

Munter und straff [Allegramente e risoluto] [♩ = 126]

Schumann wrote his *Album for the Young* (from which this comes) primarily for his eldest child's seventh birthday: he enjoyed the task so much that he composed all the pieces in just over a fortnight.

MELODY

LE COUPPEY

This comes from *ABC du piano*, one of a large number of educational albums by Félix le Couppey, who was a professor at the Paris Conservatoire (where he himself had been a pupil).

POLISH SONG

HILLER, Op.117 No.18

A close friend of Berlioz, Schumann and Mendelssohn, Ferdinand Hiller was equally distinguished as a pianist (specially noted for his powers of improvisation), conductor (throughout Germany, but also in Paris, London and St Petersburg), composer (of six operas, three concertos and three symphonies, many chamber works, songs and piano pieces), teacher and critic.

PRELUDE

HELLER, Op.119 No.9

Hungarian by birth, trained in Vienna but settling in Paris, Stephen Heller was a much admired pianist whom some critics considered even more poetic than his friend Chopin. His studies and character pieces, and two visits to London, also won him a large following in England.

AB 2077

ALLEGRETTO

LOESCHHORN, Op.65 No.4

A distinguished Berlin piano teacher (awarded the title of Royal Professor in 1858), Albert Loeschhorn also, for many years, organised a highly successful series of chamber concerts. He wrote a large number of studies for the piano which became standard educational works.

MELODY

L. KÖHLER, Op.190 No.27

After a period as a theatre conductor, Louis Köhler settled in Königsberg, where he established a very popular piano school and wrote over a dozen voluminous educational works (besides three operas, a ballet and a symphony).

AB 2077

WALTZ

GURLITT, Op.179 No.21

Cornelius Gurlitt was born in Altona (then belonging to Denmark): after teaching in Copenhagen he became a professor at the Hamburg Conservatory. His compositions were strongly influenced by Schumann.

VIVACE

GURLITT, Op.179 No.32

POCO VIVACE

KIRCHNER, Op.55 No.2

The very title of Theodor Kirchner's *New Scenes of Childhood*, from which this piece comes, proclaims him a disciple of Schumann. Before he was 20 he was, on Mendelssohn's recommendation, appointed a municipal organist in Switzerland: later he became a conductor in Zurich, director of a music school in Würzburg, and a teacher in various German cities.

AB 2077

MINUET

REINECKE, Op.183 No.3/2

A friend of Gurlitt, Carl Reinecke was in turn court pianist in Copenhagen, a professor in Cologne, director of music in Breslau, for 35 years conductor of the Leipzig Gewandhaus concerts and simultaneously, for even longer, taught at the Leipzig Conservatory. This piece comes from his *Serenade for the Young*.

ALLEGRETTO

F. WOHLFAHRT

Both Franz Wohlfahrt and his father were noted Leipzig piano teachers and writers of educational music.

GATHERING FLOWERS

WILM, Op.posth. No.4

Nicolai von Wilm studied in Leipzig, returned to his native Riga as a conductor in the municipal theatre and then taught in St Petersburg before settling first in Dresden and then in Wiesbaden. He wrote several excellent (though now neglected) chamber works and a great deal of piano music.

AB 2077

CUCKOO

E. HORÁK

The Horák piano school in Vienna, founded by Eduard and his younger brother (both Czechs), acquired a European reputation. For its pupils they both wrote a large number of piano pieces.

THE SICK DOLL

TCHAIKOVSKY, Op.39 No.7

After completing his Fourth Symphony and the opera *Evgeny Onyegin*, Tchaikovsky retired to the country near Kiev, where 'as a relaxation' he wrote the *Children's Album* from which this piece comes.

AB 2077

MR HAPPY-GO-LUCKY

SANDRÉ

Animé, avec beaucoup de rondeur [Briskly] [♩ = 126]

A peculiarity about Gustave Sandré, a professor at the Nancy Conservatoire in eastern France, is that apart from a Mass, a Serenade for strings and a couple of chamber works, nearly all his compositions were published as supplements to a magazine.

YOU CAN'T CATCH ME!

SANDRÉ

ANDANTE

M. VOGEL, Op.33 No.37

MODERATO

M. VOGEL, Op.34 No.10

Moritz Vogel studied in Leipzig, where he became an organist, singing teacher, music director and critic. Apart from a piano method and a collection of 200 partsongs (as well as other, larger choral works) he also wrote a *History of Music*.

LITTLE PIECE

D'INDY, Op.74 No.2

Immensely influential in French musical life, Vincent d'Indy, who had been a pupil of Franck and was a fervent admirer of Wagner, ran the Société Nationale de Musique and was co-founder and director of the Schola Cantorum in Paris. This piece comes from his album *For children of all ages*.

AB 2077

SMILES AFTER TEARS

FUCHS, Op.47 No.10

Robert Fuchs, composer of symphonies, five admirable Serenades for strings and much chamber music, studied at the Vienna Conservatory, where at the age of 28 he became a professor. In his 37 years in that institution (of which his elder brother, an opera conductor, became director) he numbered several leading composers among his pupils. This piece comes from his *Album for the Young*.

THE LITTLE BIRD AND THE CAT

KRUG, Op.83 No.16

A pupil of Gurlitt in his native Hamburg, and then studying in Leipzig, Arnold Krug taught in Berlin for five years, and then, after visiting France and Italy, returned to Hamburg, where he organised a choral society and became a professor at the Conservatory. He wrote a number of choral, orchestral and chamber works.

AB 2077

MORNING PASTIMES

FIBICH

Poco allegretto [♩ = 80]

Zdeněk Fibich, who at 30 gave up his posts as a conductor in Prague to devote himself exclusively to composition (eventually with 600 works to his credit), wrote this piece at the age of 18, between leaving the Leipzig Conservatory and completing his education in Paris and Mannheim.

AB 2077

WALTZ

H. J. RICHTER, Op.2 No.2

Leicht, spielend [Leggiero, scherzando] [♩. = 56]

Little is known of Hermann Julius Richter other than that he wrote a handful of songs and of easy piano pieces.

EVENING CALM

SCHÜTT, Op.105 No.6

Musically educated first in St Petersburg, where he was born of Austrian parents, and then in Leipzig (where he was a pupil of Reinecke) and Vienna (studying under the great teacher Leschetizky), Eduard Schütt toured widely as a virtuoso and became conductor of the prestigious Wagner-Verein of the Vienna Academy. Besides a comic opera, two piano concertos and several chamber works, he wrote a large number of character pieces for the piano.

LAMENT

After teaching in Moscow for nearly 20 years, Alexander Grechaninov, an extremely prolific composer in many fields, moved to Paris, earning a reputation as a conductor of his own works, but in 1939 he settled in New York and later became an American citizen.

FAIRY TALE

GRECHANINOV, Op.98 No.1

POCO LAMENTOSO

NIELSEN, Op.53 No.6

Carl Nielsen, the most significant composer Denmark has produced, was for some years conductor of the Royal Opera and of the Copenhagen Musical Society, and for a time director of the Conservatory there. His *Piano music for big and small* from which this comes was written in the year before his death.

AB 2077

THE BEAR

REBIKOV

Vladimir Rebikov, born in Siberia, received a wide musical education in Moscow, Berlin and Vienna, went on to found music societies in Odessa and in Bessarabia, and finally settled in Moscow until the last year of his life, which he spent in the Crimea. At first strongly influenced by Tchaikovsky, he later experimented with the whole-tone scale and other then advanced ideas.

CANON

F. BRAUNROTH

Ferdinand Braunroth, a professor at the Royal Conservatory in Dresden, contributed this little canon to an 1889 book of polyphonic studies for the piano by a colleague, C. H. Döring.

THE MOTH

MAIKAPAR

Allegro grazioso e volante [♩ = 116]

Samuil Maikapar, a student at the St Petersburg Conservatory, where much later he himself was a professor for 20 years, had also been a pupil of Leschetizky in Vienna. Apart from some songs, almost all his compositions are for the piano: he also wrote two books on music.

PRELUDE

NÖLCK, Op.70 No.7

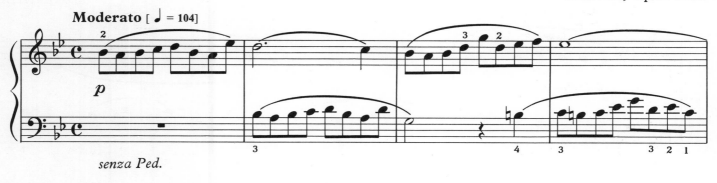

senza Ped.

August Nölck was a voluminous writer of studies and small pieces for the piano published in the first two decades of this century.

AB 2077

THE OLD WINDMILL

DUNHILL

Thomas Dunhill, a pupil of Stanford, was a music master at Eton for ten years and, for much longer, a professor at the Royal College of Music. He first made his name as a composer with several outstanding chamber works (leading to his writing a book on chamber music) and songs; but he also had a great success with his light opera *Tantivy Towers*.

ALLEGRO

DUNHILL, Op.74 Bk.1 No.3

AB 2077

RUSSIAN SONG

Allegro energico [♩ = 112]

GEDIKE, Op.36 No.24

Alexander Gedike came from a long family line of composers of German extraction, studied at the Moscow Conservatory and later became a professor there himself. Among his works are four operas to his own librettos, four concertos and three symphonies, as well as much piano music.

BARCAROLLE

GEDIKE

GLIDING

SWINSTEAD

Felix Swinstead, a Londoner, was educated at the Royal Academy of Music, where he won prestigious scholarships and at the age of 30 became a professor of piano, a post he held for the best part of half a century.

AB 2077

LULLABY

DYSON

George Dyson taught at a number of leading public schools (including Marlborough, Rugby, Wellington and Winchester), and then for 15 years was director of the Royal College of Music (where he himself had been a student and had won the Mendelssohn Scholarship).

GALOP

Allegro [♩ = 116]

KABALEVSKY, Op.39 No.18

Dmitri Kabalevsky's output includes half-a-dozen operas, six concertos and four symphonies, but much of his energies have been directed to piano music for young people. He taught composition at the Moscow Concervatory, and later held various influential posts in Soviet musical education.

AB 2077

LULLABY FOR A CHINESE INFANT

GORDON JACOB

After teaching composition at Birkbeck and Morley Colleges, Gordon Jacob, who had been a pupil of Stanford's at the Royal College of Music, joined its staff in 1926 and taught there for 40 years, numbering many distinguished British musicians among his own pupils. He was a specialist on the subject of instrumentation, and in his own compositions consistently showed consummate craftsmanship.

AB 2077

THE QUIET WOOD

MICHAEL HEAD

In 1927, two years after graduating at the Royal Academy of Music, Michael Head became a piano professor there for the rest of his life: he was also a well-known examiner. The bulk of his output as a composer consists of songs, many of which were written for himself to sing to his own accompaniment in concerts in various parts of the world.

Printed in England by Caligraving Limited Thetford Norfolk   AB 2077   1:96